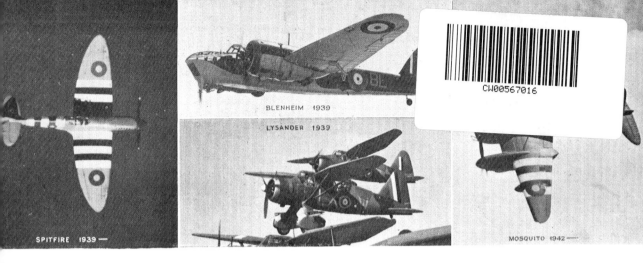

BLENHEIM 1939

LYSANDER 1939

SPITFIRE 1939 —

MOSQUITO 1942 —

PHOTOGRAPHIC RECONNAISSANCE
1939 ——————— and ——————— 1944
PHOTOGRAPHIC INTELLIGENCE

Prior to the outbreak of war it was planned that Blenheim aircraft would carry out any long range photographic reconnaissance required, while the short range photography in immediate support of Armies would be obtained by Lysanders. Accordingly, when war broke out a number of Blenheim and Lysander Squadrons were despatched to the continent as part of the Air Component of the B.E.F. From the U.K. the Blenheims of No. 2 Group Bomber Command were expected to obtain any photography required for targetting prior to bombing attacks together with any photography subsequent to attacks from which to assess the damage. It was therefore a Blenheim that took off on the 3rd Sept., 1939 to photograph the German Fleet lying off Wilhelmshaven and so completed the first photographic sortie of the war.

But the difficulties and dangers of photographic reconnaissance under war conditions were far greater than had been anticipated and of 42 sorties flown by the Air Component during the last three months of 1939, eight failed to return and twenty produced no photographs, in spite of the fact that no deep penetrations were made. Unescorted Blenheims flying by day into enemy territory, at heights under 20,000 feet and in clear conditions suitable for photography, had little chance of survival. Portions of the Siegfried Line were certainly photographed at a cost, but photography of the all-important Ruhr district proved almost impossible and it was clear that some new technique was essential.

The obvious solution was an aircraft which could fly sufficiently fast and sufficiently high to avoid interception. R.A.E. Farnborough, charged with the responsibility of producing such an aircraft, selected the Spitfire for their experiments. The latter was then making its first appearance in any quantity and was the only aircraft available possessing the necessary performance. The first step was the removal of the armament so that long range tanks and cameras could be carried.

At that time the standard F.24 was virtually the only camera available in the R.A.F., and being comparatively small the easiest way to install the cameras was in the wings, so that the original two Spitfires had a vertical F.24 (F.L. 5″) camera mounted in each wing. These two Spitfires were moved to Heston at the end of 1939, where they became known as the "Heston Special Flight," and experimental operational sorties were started forthwith.

The experiments were an immediate success in that deep penetrations were made at once without interference from the enemy but the method of operating raised numerous problems, some of which were not to be solved until some time later. These problems related to Navigation, Equipment and Endurance. When the experiments started, the available oxygen equipment was by modern standards quite elementary yet for the first time a pilot was expected to operate for hours at a time at heights over 30,000 feet and it was not known to what extent the human frame could tolerate such conditions. On the navigation side the problem was quite new. Previous photography had been carried out in an aircraft such as the Blenheim in which the flight lines were directed by an observer through a form of bomb-sight. With the Spitfire however the pilot had not only to fly the aircraft but also to navigate it with considerable accuracy. Moreover, he could not see the ground detail immediately below the aircraft, or for ten miles on either side. Experience had therefore to evolve a system for navigating on detail some ten miles to one side. Finally on the equipment side the first major issue related to the cameras. These had been designed on the old conception, i.e., that photographs would be taken at a little over 10,000 feet. At such a height focal lengths of 5″ and 8″ would have provided photographs of adequate scale to identify major military installations but when the same cameras were used to obtain photographs from over 30,000 feet the scale was inevitably so small that useful military intelligence could not be

Continued on next page.

1

extracted. Nor could simple enlargement of these photographs meet the difficulty as the details sought were in fact about the same size as the grain of the film and consequently impossible to resolve even at high magnifications.

Many other operational problems also arose during the early days owing to the extremely low temperatures encountered at high altitudes, which resulted for instance in the freezing of the accumulator which operated the cameras, a problem gradually overcome by introduction of hot air from the engine. A more serious problem, which was not solved to full satisfaction until much later in the war related to the camera mounting. The main difficulty was to evolve some method of holding a camera in position which would eliminate all vibration from the aircraft.

Some of the early sorties represented definite milestones which went far to prove the efficacy of the new theory of reconnaissance. On the 10th Feb., 1940, Emden and Wilhelmshaven were photographed for the first time and in March virtually the whole of the Ruhr was photographed in one flight, and the mosaic made from the result still remains the standard briefing material for this all-important area of Germany. These sorties while proving conclusively that the future of photographic reconnaissance lay with the fast high flying machine, also showed that new cameras and lenses would have to be designed if photographs of a large enough scale for detailed interpretation were to be produced. Moreover, since the range of the first Spitfires was only adequate to touch the fringe of Germany a period of very active development began not only in cameras but also in trials and experiments to lengthen operational range.

Continued on page 4.

(Plate 1.) The first reconnaissance sortie of the "Heston Special Flight" was made on 18th November, 1939, the target intended to be covered was Aachen, but the anticipated difficulties of navigation proved well founded and the result of this first effort was some photographs south of Aachen on the Belgian side of the frontier. The contact print reproduced here is from this first sortie, it covers the village of Bullingen and was taken with an F.24 camera and 5 ins. lens from 33,000 ft. giving a scale of 1 : 79,200. (See also opposite page.)

(Plates 2 & 3.) The second and third sorties of the "Heston Special Flight" were taken on 21st December, 1939 and a fourth on 22nd and between these three sorties a large part of the Seigfried Line and areas between Saarbrucken and Aachen were covered. Even though the scale of the photographs was too small for detailed interpretation, these flights went a long way towards proving the effectiveness of this new technique in photographic reconnaissance.

TRIER 2

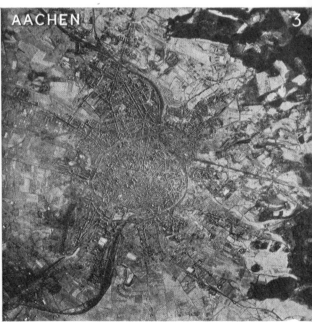

AACHEN 3

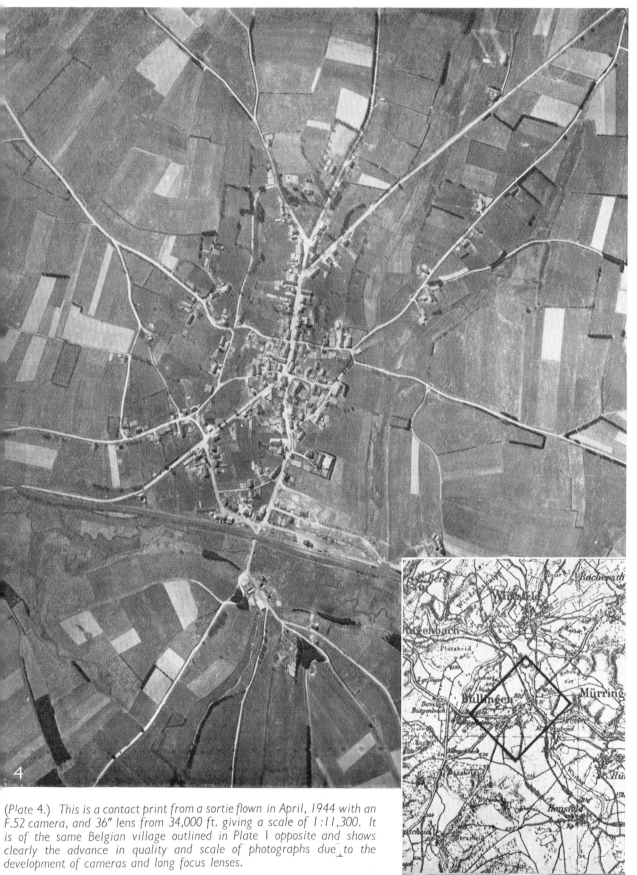

4

(Plate 4.) This is a contact print from a sortie flown in April, 1944 with an
F.52 camera, and 36" lens from 34,000 ft. giving a scale of 1:11,300. It
is of the same Belgian village outlined in Plate 1 opposite and shows
clearly the advance in quality and scale of photographs due to the
development of cameras and long focus lenses.

3

(Plate 5.) *Invasion barges are seen in hundreds in the Channel port of Calais in Sept., 1940, when Germany was preparing for the assault on this country. Air reconnaissance enabled a constant watch to be kept on the operations although the scale of the photographs did not allow for detailed interpretation.*

DOBRIC FJORD

(Plate 6.) *The picture of the 'Bismarck,' taken by photographic reconnaissance pilot in May, 1941, when t warship lay at anchor in Dobric Fjord, which began t sequence of events terminating in the destruction of th formidable German battleship.*

After many types of aircraft had been considered and tried out the Spitfire was still accepted as being the most suitable. By adding a 30-gallon bulge tank in the port wing Kiel was brought into range in April, 1940, while on the camera side, to ease the navigational problem over large targets such as ports, two cameras were mounted side by side, each tilted in opposite directions about 10 degrees from the vertical so that double the amount of ground was covered per flight on two parallel strips of country with a small overlap. These two cameras were accommodated in a similar bulge in the starboard wing of the new Spitfire. The photography of Kiel was another major milestone. A large concentration of shipping was seen, but there being no previous photography of the port to form a basis for comparison it was impossible to know whether such a state was normal or abnormal to the port. With the invasion of Norway two days later the significance was at once apparent, proving the necessity of regular reconnaissance to provide comparison cover without which such unusual incidents could not be recognised. At this stage in the war however there was no general appreciation of the potentialities of photographic reconnaissance and in any case the small scale photographs obtained during the early sorties, with limited military value, had done little to prove what could be expected in the future with

the right equipment and training. Older methods o obtaining information about the enemy were still reliec upon mainly to meet all intelligence needs. With the fall o France however the situation changed almost overnight since obviously all information previously derived through the French Deuxieme Bureau was lost and at the same time the enemy was in occupation of huge new areas of Europe for which little in the way of intelligence organisation hac been provided. Comprehensive photographic reconnaissance, therefore, still in the experimental stage became a vital necessity and from being a minor aid hac to be developed at the utmost speed into a major source of information.

At first only sufficient aircraft were available to photograph the invasion ports where the whole build-up o the intended attack against this country was watched day by day. Later however as more aircraft became available an increasing number of targets inland were photographed, starting with airfields and later extending to railways, industries, etc. Yet even then the information later to be obtained was only forecast to a smal extent and it was not until a large number of photograph had been obtained and the job carried on for many months that empirical experience began to revea enormous potentialities. *Continued at top of page 6*

(Plate 7.) Part of the Italian port of Spezia which was photographed in an epic flight by a P.R. Spitfire in April, 1941. Owing to weather the pilot had to fly blind through cloud from the English Coast to Genoa seeing only the Alps en route. Conditions improved over the target and he was able to photograph his objectives from 24,000 feet, but on the return trip he again met thick cloud. Due to strong head winds his petrol became very low and he was getting ready to bale out when he sighted the white cliffs of Dover. Gliding in he made a perfect landing in a pole-studded field. He had been airborne for 7 hrs. 10 mins. The aircraft sustained no damage and after the removal of a few poles it was flown back to base the next day.

(Plate 8.) On the night of 3/4th March, 1942, BOMBER COMMAND aircraft attacked the Renault Works at Billancourt. The following day a P.R. aircraft took off in heavy rain and poor visibility to photograph the damage, flying by instruments in 10/10 cloud until breaking cloud near the target at 500 feet and proceeding to photograph the damage from as low as 400 feet. On the return journey he met with similar conditions, at one time being at 0 feet over the Channel. At 800 feet over land he was still in 10/10 but eventually landed safely. The illustration, left, shows one of the fine oblique photographs which were obtained and brought back in the face of such appalling conditions.

Towards the end of 1941 the adaptation of the Mosquito aircraft for photographic reconnaissance opened up vast new areas, including Eastern Germany, the Baltic ports, and much of Northern Norway. Southern Norway had already been photographed regularly by Spitfires, in spite of the exceptionally long sea crossing in a single engined aircraft without a navigator. From this period onwards however, very considerable advances were made in the development of the reconnaissance Spitfires and Mosquitos. These took the form of increased speed, ceiling, range and versatility, which in their turn led to corresponding increases in the scope and variety of the work so that more and more of the enemy's essential military activities came under constant supervision.

None of this, however, would have been possible without a corresponding development of the cameras. Gradually cameras of new types and with greater focal lengths were developed which reached fruition with the production of the modern F.52 camera, the latter having a negative size 9″ by 7″ with focal lengths up to 36″. This enabled photographs at a scale of about 1:10,000 to be obtained from the maximum ceiling, i.e., at heights up to 40,000 feet. At such scales, the type of traffic in the railway sidings, the state of U-boat construction, or the layout of a Radar installation, to quote just three examples, can be studied.

Even so, many problems remained which could not be answered by photographs even of scales as large as 1:10,000. For instance, having located Radar stations, it then became of importance to study their structural detail and if possible obtain photographs which would enable measurements of the array to be made. These requirements were met by the reconnaissance units in the early stages by fitting an oblique camera into a Spitfire and obtaining photographs from heights as low as 50 feet. Later in the war however other problems arose, notably during the period of flying bomb operations against this country when a requirement arose for vertical photography at scales as large as 1:2,000 At such scales, the velocity of the aircraft across the target is such that considerable movement is apparent on the negative. A camera was therefore developed, based on an American idea, for moving the negative during exposure at sufficient speed to compensate for ground movement.

Numerous other installations to meet yet other problems were evolved. These included cameras in the nose of a Mosquito for beach reconnaissance, and two oblique cameras, one in either wing, to record stereoscopically surf conditions of beaches prior to landings, etc. Each new development involved, of course, in its turn, the development of new tactics, many of which could only be evolved in the face of actual enemy reaction, which to single low level aircraft in the neighbourhood of his vital targets was normally violent in the extreme.

Continued on page 8

(Plate 9.) *Many rumours were prevalent regarding the scuttling of the French Fleet before the question was finally settled by air photographs which revealed the destruction of the greater part of the Fleet in Toulon harbour on the 28th Nov., 1942.*

(Plate 10.) *Prior to the attack on the Mohne Dam the water level of the reservoir was constantly watched on air photographs to assist in choosing the right moment to make the assault. A few hours after the raid on the night of 16/17th May, 1943, a P.R. pilot took this striking picture of the great breach and the release of over a million tons of water.*

(Plate 11.) *An enlargement from a P.R. sortie flown over the devastated city and port of Hamburg shortly after the heavy night attacks by BOMBER COMMAND in July, 1943. The excellent quality and scale of such photography allows interpretation of a most detailed nature.*

(Plate 12.) A fine low oblique shot, taken in March, 1944 by a P.R. Mosquito with side-facing oblique camera, showing the heavy damage caused by 12,000 lb. bombs to the Gnome and Rhone aero-engine works at Limoges.

Nor has photographic reconnaissance been limited to day work. Much research in night reconnaissance has been carried out during the last two years and many successful sorties obtained. In this type of photography a series of single exposures is obtained by dropping successive flash bombs which are timed to detonate at given heights above the ground. Many experiments have been needed to find out the optimum height at which the bomb should burst in relation to the aircraft, and much experience in navigating correctly over a target at night has been gained.

In conclusion, the war experience of reconnaissance has shown the absolute necessity for continual development not only of aircraft, tactics and cameras, but also of interpretation technique. It has shown the enormous extent to which results were dependent on the training and experience of the individual personnel carrying out the work, and finally it has shown that very complete information indeed on the enemy's activity can be obtained throughout the whole of his territory provided that photographic reconnaissance is carried out on a sufficient scale, i.e., that his vital areas are all photographed regularly. With such a watch the many surprises which he was able to bring off during the early stages of the war are virtually impossible.

(Plate 13.) Some of the finest examples of low oblique photography are to be found in sorties covering Radar sites where close-ups are essential in order that tiny details in the layout may be studied. Below is such an example. It shows a Radar installation in the Zealand district of Denmark photographed by a P.R. aircraft from practically 0 feet.

(*Plate 14.*) *On the 12th July, 1944, a P.R. aircraft set out to find the ' Tirpitz '. Thick cloud predominated off the Norwegian coast, but there were some breaks at lower altitudes, and the pilot flew at varying levels until the ' Tirpitz ' and attendant ships were suddenly spotted obliquely from 15,000 feet. Down went the aircraft in an extremely steep dive, pulling out at 9,000 feet at cloud base, when the top escape hatch suddenly blew off and disappeared. Despite this calamity two runs were made over the target and oblique and vertical photographs obtained. On the return journey the crew almost froze because of the draught from the broken hatchway but got back safely after a round trip of over 2,300 miles. Below is one of the excellent vertical photographs which were obtained of this once formidable battleship.*

AIR CAMERAS AND EQUIPMENT FOR PHOTOGRAPHIC RECONNAISSANCE

The development of British air cameras during the present war has followed closely upon the changes in operational tactics made necessary as a result of early P.R. experience during 1939 and 1940.

At the outbreak of the war in 1939, virtually the only air camera in general service in the R.A.F. was the Type F.24 with lenses of 5″, 8″, 14″ and 20″ focal lengths, and a magazine capacity of 125 exposures, these being employed in all the types of aircraft then used for photographic reconnaissance. The principal types of aircraft concerned were the Lysander, Battle and Blenheim, but it soon became apparent that these had not the performance necessary to penetrate the enemy defences, and it therefore became imperative to employ high performance aircraft which would rely on their speed and ceiling for security. The Spitfire was first selected for this role, and one F.24-5″ camera was installed in each wing. The introduction of the P.R. Mosquito early in 1942 was a further big step forward in photographic reconnaissance, as it enabled the radius of action to be considerably increased.

The principle of using a high performance fighter for P.R. was quickly proved, but its successful application was beset by innumerable difficulties, not least of which was the resultant small scale produced by the F.24 camera when used at high altitudes, and the necessity of heating the cameras to withstand the intense cold encountered high up. The difficulty of interpretation from the very small scales obtained led to a greater demand for lenses of longer focal length, and for a camera giving a larger size of negative, and consequently increased cover.

To meet this demand, the F.8 camera Marks II and III were introduced, these cameras being fitted with 20″ and 36″ lenses respectively, and a magazine capable of taking up to 250 exposures. Later, the F.52 camera was introduced into the R.A.F., the main advantages of this type of camera over the F.8 being a larger capacity magazine (up to 500 exposures) and the fact that as the gear box is practically identical with that used with the F.24 camera, a considerable lessening of production problems is effected. The F.52 camera employs lenses of 14″, 20″ and 36″ focal lengths to cover a wide range of requirements.

In the early types of P.R. Spitfire and Mosquito aircraft, the practice was to use the vertical cameras singly, an installation which produced comparatively narrow cover when the longer focal lenses were used. To increase the lateral cover, a modified installation was introduced incorporating two cameras, tilted in such a way that the lateral cover was approximately doubled. This came to be known as a " split " installation, and today is the normal practice in all types of P.R. aircraft except where the requirement is for survey photography.

The problem of supplying heat to the cameras to prevent freezing up, and the formation of condensation on the camera lenses, was initially overcome by mounting the cameras in the wing sufficiently near to the engine to receive its heat. Later, when the cameras were fitted into the fuselage of the aircraft, electric heaters were introduced, but were ultimately replaced by a system whereby a closed camera compartment was provided into which hot air from the engine was fed.

Simultaneously with the development of new types of cameras, the development of associated camera equipment proceeded apace, and included many improvements in the design of camera controls, mountings, etc.

To meet the necessity of taking photographs from all heights under difficult weather conditions, new camera installations had to be developed, new types of cameras produced, and different tactics employed. This has led to the introduction and use in the R.A.F. of moving film cameras, also the employment of forward facing oblique cameras, both singly and in pairs, to give stereo cover.

The moving film camera provides a means of compensating for image movement due to the forward velocity of the aircraft during exposure, thus permitting much larger scales to be obtained than is possible with standard cameras, and, within limits, permitting of longer exposures where necessary.

Several types of moving film cameras have been developed for the R.A.F. to meet varying operational requirements. In general there are at present two main types of moving film cameras in use for Photographic Reconnaissance.

(a) *Moving Film Strip Cameras.* With these cameras, the moving film is caused to pass over a narrow slit positioned near the focal plane, at a speed equal to that of the ground image, the resultant negative taking the form of a continuous strip. Both F.24 and F.52 type cameras have been adapted for this purpose, for use with 5″ or 8″ lenses. These cameras are employed principally for low-level vertical photography.

(b) *Moving Film with Focal Plane Shutter (Type F.63 camera)* The Type 63 camera consists essentially of an F.52 camera specially modified to enable the film to move near to the desired compensated speed as possible throughout the time that the camera is operating. It is used for carrying out large scale photography from medium altitudes with long focal length lenses. The camera employs a focal plane shutter giving runaway exposures approximately every second.

Forward facing camera installations for stereo oblique cover have been installed in both Mosquito and Spitfire aircraft, for low level use, and are often employed in conjunction with the vertical moving film strip cameras.

Following the entry of the U.S.A. in the present war, various types of American cameras were obtained by the R.A.F. The main types concerned were the K.17-6″ and K.8AB-12″ cameras for survey and mapping photography, and the K.19 type cameras for night photography.

In conclusion, it may be stated that, assisted as it has been by the impetus of war requirements, the development of air cameras and associated equipment during the war has been tremendous, and has enabled the R.A.F. to provide the best Photographic Reconnaissance yet achieved.

F.24 CAMERAS
(250 EXPOSURE MAGAZINES)

14"   8"   5"   3¼"

F.52 CAMERAS
(500 EXPOSURE MAGAZINES)

MODIFIED AS MOVING FILM STRIP CAMERAS

     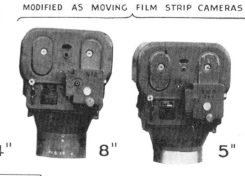

36"   20"   14"   8"   5"

FAIRCHILD 'K' CAMERAS

K19B 12"   K8AB 12"   K17 6"

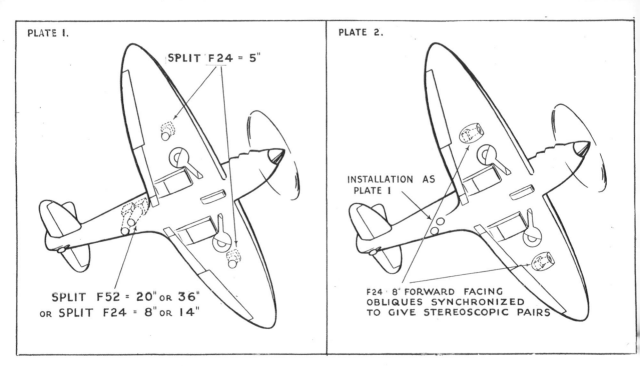

PLATE 1.

SPLIT F24 = 5"

SPLIT F52 = 20" OR 36"
OR SPLIT F24 = 8" OR 14"

PLATE 2.

INSTALLATION AS
PLATE 1

F24 8" FORWARD FACING
OBLIQUES SYNCHRONIZED
TO GIVE STEREOSCOPIC PAIRS

CAMERA INSTALLATIONS IN THE RECONNAISSANCE SPITFIRE

The diagrams above are typical camera installations in the reconnaissance Spitfire. Plate 1 : High altitude split vertical layout. Plate 2 : Low altitude forward facing oblique, F.24-8" cameras are used for this installation. Below: The first F.24 camera with 5" lens to be installed in a Spitfire wing by the R.A.E. during October, 1939.

CAMERA MOTOR

F24 CAMERA

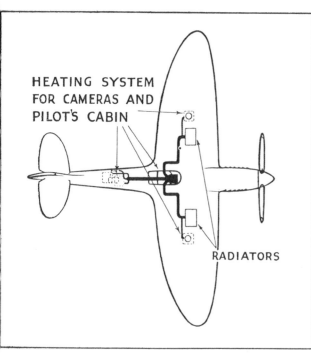

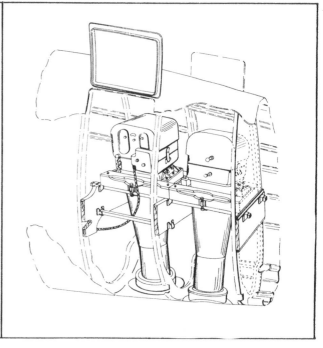

CAMERA HEATING

Diagram of camera heating in Spitfire which is produced by hot air from the cooling system.

CAMERA INSTALLATION

Installation of the F.52-36″ split vertical camera with 36″ lenses in a Spitfire fuselage.

FANNED CAMERAS HALVE THE NECESSARY NUMBER OF RUNS OVER A TARGET

The diagram and annotated photograph (below) show how a 5° 20′ inclination to the vertical of the fanned F.52-36″ cameras allows a 10 per cent. lateral overlap and when the two cameras are working together they cover nearly twice the area of a single vertical.

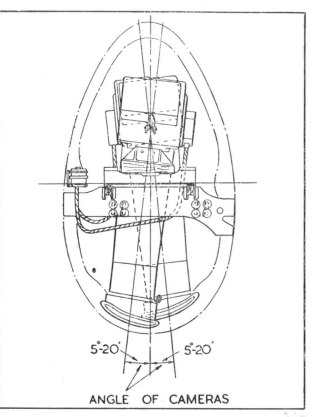

5°-20′   5°-20′

ANGLE OF CAMERAS

CAMERA INSTALLATIONS IN THE P.R. MOSQUITO

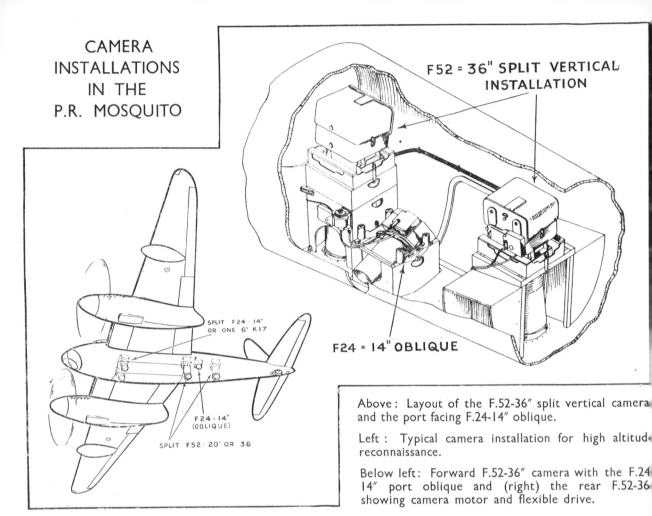

F52 = 36" SPLIT VERTICAL INSTALLATION

F24 = 14" OBLIQUE

SPLIT F24·14" OR ONE 6" K17

F24·14" (OBLIQUE)

SPLIT F52·20" OR 36"

Above: Layout of the F.52-36" split vertical camera and the port facing F.24-14" oblique.

Left: Typical camera installation for high altitude reconnaissance.

Below left: Forward F.52-36" camera with the F.24-14" port oblique and (right) the rear F.52-36" showing camera motor and flexible drive.

F.24-14" forward facing oblique in Mosquito starboard wing drop tank.

F.24-8" forward facing oblique installation in bulge on Spitfire port wing.

FORWARD FACING
STEREOSCOPIC OBLIQUES

The fitting of forward facing oblique cameras in the wing drop tanks of Mosquitos and in bulges on Spitfire wings has made stereoscopic cover of important targets possible. A great amount of skill and daring on the part of the pilot is necessary as this type of photography is carried out at zero feet, often necessitating a steep bank on approaching the target to avoid crashing into it. This type of reconnaissance can be carried out in dull weather by the use of lenses with an aperture of f/2.9.

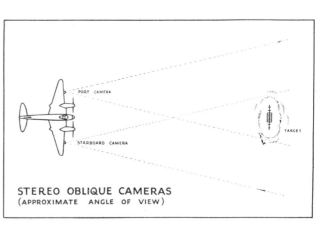

STEREO OBLIQUE CAMERAS
(APPROXIMATE ANGLE OF VIEW)

Stereoscopic Oblique of Radar Chimney

LOW ALTITUDE PHOTOGRAPHY OF IMPORTANT INSTALLATION

Examples from a sortie taken by a single F.52-10" forward facing oblique camera fitted in the nose of a Mosquito. The target was an important installation under observation during the battle against the flying bomb. With the forward facing camera the pilot can navigate straight on to the target and be more certain of obtaining photographs than by flying around it as is necessary with a side facing camera ; when flying under difficult conditions banking may cause the camera to miss part of the target. The illustrations on these two pages (Plates 1-4) show four consecutive shots of the target and a plot of the run up.

Plate 5 : A typical Mosquito layout for low altitude forward facing oblique and vertical photography.

Plate 6 : The single F.52-14" in the nose of the Mosquito.

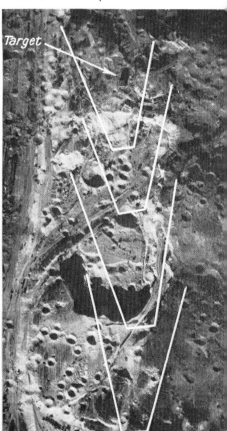

Target

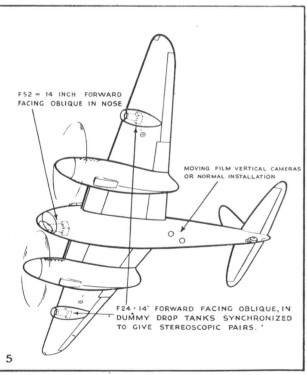

F52 = 14 INCH FORWARD FACING OBLIQUE IN NOSE

MOVING FILM VERTICAL CAMERAS OR NORMAL INSTALLATION

F24·14" FORWARD FACING OBLIQUE, IN DUMMY DROP TANKS SYNCHRONIZED TO GIVE STEREOSCOPIC PAIRS.'

SIDE OBLIQUE AND MOVING FILM

A port facing F.24 oblique mounted in a Mustang behind the pilot's cockpit (Plate 1) and a typical operational oblique taken with this installation over Walcheren Island (Plate 2). Plate 3 shows a vertical moving film installation under the port wing of a Typhoon. Plates 4 and 5 are two examples taken with moving film cameras from medium altitude.

CAMERA CONTROLS IN P.R. AIRCRAFT

DISTRIBUTION BOX TYPE 48

TYPE 35 CONTROL

CAMERA CONTROL PANEL IN P.R. MOSQUITO

Remote controls for all cameras are situated in the pilot's cockpit allowing selection of each camera individually for specific targets.

TYPE 35 CONTROL

CAMERA WARNING LIGHTS

CAMERA SELECTOR SWITCHES

MASTER SWITCH

CAMERA CONTROLS IN SPITFIRE

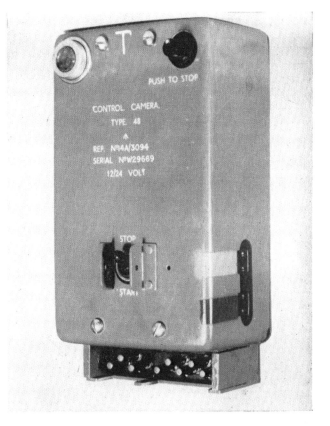

PUSH TO STOP

CONTROL CAMERA.
TYPE. 48

REF. Nº14A/3094
SERIAL Nº W29669
12/24 VOLT

STOP
START

TYPE 48 CONTROL

PHOTOGRAPHIC INTELLIGENCE

INTRODUCTORY REMARKS

Photographic Intelligence, or Interpretation, usually known as P.I. for short, is of course only one of the many sources for obtaining intelligence about the enemy. It is, however, an extremely important one, for a number of reasons, some of which are discussed below.

The first reason for the importance of P.I. lies in the fact that photographs provide positive evidence, as opposed to hints and indications which come from most sources — evidence upon which an operation can be planned. For example, doubtless various sources of intelligence indicated that the Tirpitz had moved down the Norwegian coast to TROMSO. On such information, however, the attack by Bomber Command with 12,000 lb. bombs which sank her could not have been planned. It required air photographs which showed the exact berth she was occupying, the extent of her camouflage, the anti-aircraft defences around her, and so on.

The second reason for the importance lies in the speed with which this source can provide intelligence. Clearly, there is a time factor in the supply of information from every source, but with P.I. the factor is comparatively small, in fact a matter of hours. It is merely a question of how long the photographic section requires to develop and print the photographs, plus the time needed by the interpreter to form his opinion. After that, the telephone will do the rest.

The third reason is the fact that large areas of enemy territory can be photographed in one flight and subsequently examined, from many different points of view. This means that if all the reconnaissance aircraft are sent out on a co-ordinated plan, even if the whole of Germany is not covered in one day, a sufficient cross-section of his activity is picked up to give a good picture of his overall activity.

The fourth reason lies in the difficulty of bluffing against a proper reconnaissance programme. Whereas it is possible to plant false information for the benefit of most sources, against this particular source, within its scope, this is largely impossible.

Again, as a source it is relatively secure. This is of particular importance in planning major operations, which inevitably require much detailed intelligence on the operational area. Normally it is not possible to increase the flow of information coming in from most sources on a particular area without breaking security, whereas with P.I. it is merely a question of taking existing photographs from a library, if they exist, and re-examining them from the new point of view.

It would be foolish, however, to think that P.I. provides all the answers required by intelligence. Far from it. In fact it suffers from certain disadvantages, the greatest of which are weather, range of aircraft, and the problem of having an aircraft over the right place at the right time.

Weather is perhaps the greatest of the handicaps, and obviously during bad weather periods we are entirely dependent on our other sources of intelligence for our day to day information.

Range is no longer a prohibitive handicap in Europe, since if necessary any part of Germany can be photographed today. On the other hand, in the Pacific P.I. can play little part at present in telling us what is happening in Japan, and we must rely on other means until we secure a closer base from which to operate.

Finally, there are many questions which P.I. could never answer, enemy morale being an obvious enough case. There are many other questions which it could answer if an aircraft happened to be overhead at the precise moment that something was happening. But this is hardly to be expected so that unless the activity is of reasonable duration it will be found only by lucky chance. Still, so many photographs are taken today that many lucky chances occur and little of major importance passes unnoticed.

The next few pages are an attempt to describe in some detail a few of the actual results which have been achieved. They show that the subject is a varied one and covers a very wide and considerable field.

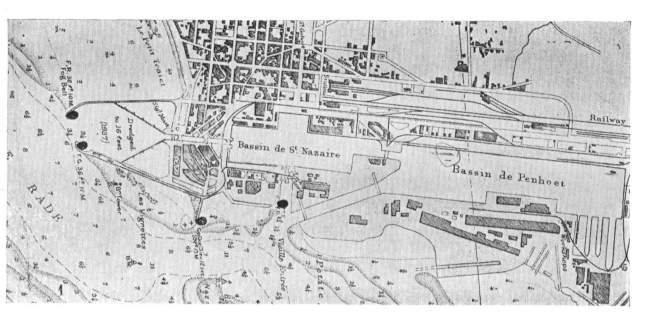

COMBINED OPERATIONS – ST. NAZAIRE
(MARCH, 1942)

The St. Nazaire Combined Operations attack of 26th—28th March, 1942 is here given as an example of the indispensable part played by aerial photography in the planning and preparations for such an undertaking. A model was required by the planners and the only available map of the port at that time was the Admiralty Chart (*Plate* 1), comparison with the photographs shows how limited and inadequate this to be. So that as well as filling the gaps in this plan photographs taken up to the time of the attack also allowed new building developments to be followed and understood, i.e., U-boat shelters (A) as well as the inclusion of camouflage (B).

Apart from the use of the actual model to the planners, photographs of the model were possible from any approach and in any required lighting conditions (night or day effects) for the information and familiarisation of the participating forces (*Plates* 5, 6, and 7); they were thus able to get an impression of the port in, as nearly as possible, the conditions under which they would actually be carrying out the attack. From the photographic cover available of the port the model was finally constructed from four sorties taken over a period of 8 or 9 months (*Plates* 2 and 3 (vertical) and 4 (oblique) are selected photographs from three of these sorties).

A print from one of the sorties used for the construction of the model. Compare this with the Admiralty chart in Plate 1.

Continued on the following two pages.

Measurements based on shadow factors of all the individual buildings and quays were calculated; detailed plans and sections were produced for the construction of land form and topographical detail. The scale at which the model was produced made it possible to show changes in ground level and surface detail of three to four feet and above. Objects less than three feet were indicated by surface painting. During the construction of the model constant stereoscopic inspection of all vertical photographs was pursued while study of the oblique photographs provided information on elevations. The model was finished in October, 1941. With its help it was possible for the meticulous planning and briefing which, combined with the coolness and skill of the actual direction of the operation, enabled the " Campbeltown " and her accompanying force to cover more than 400 miles of enemy-patrolled waters and to arrive at the lock gate at 1.34 a.m., on 28th March, 1942, only 4 minutes late on schedule. Subsequent photographs (*Plates* 8 and 9 on the following page) proved the attack to have been highly successful and showed the huge caisson buckled and off its sill (C). This meant that the only dock on the Atlantic seaboard capable of taking the " Tirpitz " was completely unserviceable and likely to remain so for some time. It was not until several months later, after the dock had been drained and sealed off, that the wreck of the " Campbeltown " (D) was revealed. It is interesting to note the progress of the U-boat shelters and the new locks (E) over the period of 23 months covered by these photographs.

Vertical (above), taken before the construction of the U-boat shelters had started, and oblique (below), prints from two other sorties used for the model construction.

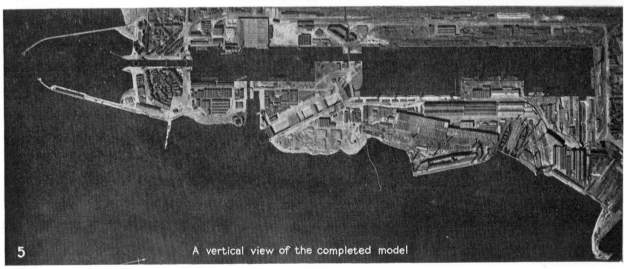

A vertical view of the completed model

Two oblique photographs of the model.
Above : Looking into the mouth of the U-boat shelters.
Below : Showing the South lock (with camouflage netting) centrally.

Final assessment from photographs taken after the action.
Plate 8 : Taken a week after the attack shows the gate destroyed (C) and the lock flooded and unserviceable. The wreck of the ' Campbeltown ' was not visible until the lock had been drained.
Plate 9 : Taken several months later shows the lock drained and dammed up, with the wreck of the ' Campbeltown ' (D) and construction of new locks (E).

DAMAGE ASSESSMENT

The main object in the planning of air operations against the enemy is to ensure that the maximum amount of damage is inflicted on the enemy's war machine at the minimum cost to ourselves, and to achieve this aim accurate damage assessment is essential. Damage assessment indicates not only the point at which the forces of attack may be profitably diverted from one target to another, but also shows the particular moment when a target previously put out of action should be reattacked. Assessment of the results of an attack have been of vital importance in formating future bombing policy, while detailed analysis of damage to industries, ports and shipbuilding yards has been indispensable to the waging of economic warfare. The bulk of the available information on damage to enemy targets is supplied from the interpretation of air photographs.

The development of damage assessment from air photographs has been closely associated with the growth of the bomber offensive. Yet despite the enormous increase in amount and variety of the damage inflicted, interpretation has tended to become more and more detailed and specialised in its application. There are now five different classifications used in the assessment of damage and the information supplied includes not only damage resulting from strategic and tactical bombing but also embraces clearance, repair and reconstruction, bombfall plotting, detailed industrial damage analysis, weapon behaviour, confirmation of ground reports, damages from causes other than bombing, and reports on specified installations of particular interest to Military Intelligence.

The above illustration, showing cumulative damage to the Hoesch-Benzin Synthetic Oil Plant (A) and the Hoesch Rolling Mills (B), is taken from a P.R. sortie flown over the DORTMUND area a few hours after a night attack on the city by aircraft of BOMBER COMMAND. It is a good example of the excellent photographs which are obtained of the Ruhr industrial area despite its being one of the most heavily defended spots in the world.

Hardly has the last bomber departed before the P.R. aircraft is on the scene photographing the damage. Often the smoke pall, although evidence of a successful attack, prevents accurate damage assessment so that only a provisional report is issued until such time as good cover can be obtained. Plate 2 (above) shows part of the burning town of Darmstadt after a night attack by BOMBER COMMAND. Plate 3 shows a part of the devastation by fire and H.E. and was taken a week after the assault was delivered on the city.

BOMB DECOYS

Aerial photography has proved to be the only accurate means of studying the enemy's decoy system. From daylight photographs it has been possible to recognise and pinpoint all types of decoys which are known to be in use, and from a detailed study of night photographs a knowledge has been gained of how these are used, and how successful they have proved.

There is no evidence that decoys were in use prior to the Battle of Britain, but after that, when it became apparent to the enemy that he would have to prepare for an air offensive over Occupied and German Territory, the construction of decoys was begun. Probably the first targets to be protected in this way were the bomber airfields in France from which the air blitz on this country was to be launched. These were quickly followed by fire sites in the industrial areas of Western Germany, and a few decoys for vulnerable oil plants. Whereas a decoy for an airfield or an oil plant is easily recognisable on air photographs, the fire sites at first presented a considerable problem, as there was no evidence at all as to how they were constructed and their appearance on a vertical photograph was quite unknown. The first clue was obtained when about 100 craters were photographed in open country, E. of the Ruhr, all concentrated within a 2-mile radius. At the focal point of this concentration were three rectangular structures, for which no other explanation could be found than that they were some form of decoy. Subsequently a number of similar structures were found, most of them with craters around them, and from good quality photographs it was reasonably deduced that they were fire sites. This has since been proved by night photographs of these sites in action.

From this initial discovery it has been possible to build up the whole story of the enemy's decoy system, and trace its many developments. As our raids have increased in weight, frequency and range, so the decoys have increased in size and numbers. A modern fire site is totally different from the original rectangular type, and may cover an area of well over 50 acres.

Industrial decoys have likewise become much more numerous; the targets served by decoys are usually oil plants or aircraft factories, though other big factories may also be represented. With heavy day attacks rocking German industrial areas, several decoys, exact replicas, on a smaller scale of their targets, have appeared, and when in action emit smoke and steam to simulate activity.

Several of the major cities of Germany are provided with enormous decoys representing the main features of the city itself. These are not designed for daylight deception but are made up of complicated lighting systems and fire sites, perhaps augmented with dummy buildings.

The success of this elaborate decoy system has been mixed. Poor weather always helps the decoys, especially where there are no obvious landmarks. Even under the present system of instrument bombing a few aircraft are misled by various new decoy devices, though it is rare now for a major diversion to be caused by decoys alone. However, should a diversion occur for any reason, decoys may be employed to hold the attack off the target. But under good weather conditions it has frequently been found from a study of the night photographs that a raid has fallen square on some doomed town whilst the decoys have been burning completely ignored, in a circle around it.

ILLUSTRATIONS

Plate 1: The Famous SKODA ARMS WORKS at PILZEN.
Plate 2: An almost exact replica of the actual works which was located in open country a short distance away. In view of the attention to detail it was presumably built to serve both a day and night function.
Plate 3: (Top, opposite page).
The decoy to the POLITZ Synthetic Oil Plant.
Plate 4: The first decoy fire site to be located.
Plate 5: A modern decoy fire site covering 70/80 acres.

CAMOUFLAGE

Throughout the war the enemy has placed great emphasis on camouflage to conceal his activities.

During the early days he confined it to objects of tactical importance, but the realisation in 1941 that a long struggle lay ahead and the necessity to guard vital installations all over Europe against the growing severity and accuracy of our air offensive, as well as to conceal their activities from the aerial camera, led him to embark upon a camouflage programme of an extremely elaborate and extensive nature. The results achieved some success in confusing the naked eye of the observer from the air, but apart from a few exceptional cases of small structures such as gun posts they failed to deceive the camera, for the latter's ability to record small details and at the same time give a picture of the whole was exploited by the interpreter to expose the enemy's most ingenious efforts. Previous photographic cover has, of course, proved invaluable.

So the aircrews still blasted the right targets and the aerial cameras still brought home the answers, and the enemy must have realised that his schemes were a failure. From about 1943 he began to confine his efforts to hastily applied disruptive painting which tended to make the target rather more conspicuous on air photographs. Only in the case of the flying bomb ramps was the old ingenuity exercised. He relied more and more upon vast smoke screens which have proved at times a handicap to both bomber and P.R. aircraft. Air photographs of these screens in action however provided information concerning position, extent, pattern and density, so that it has been possible to brief aircrews as to the conditions to be expected over the target and how best to minimise the effect of the smoke pall.

Illustrations below :

Plates 1 & 2   Factory before and after camouflage.
Plate 3   Camouflaged aircraft hangars.
Plate 4   Camouflaged water landmark.

MILITARY INTERPRETATION.

All the photographs reproduced on these two pages are shown at the scale at which they were interpreted.

The growth of this three-gun (arrows) super heavy Coastal battery near CALAIS was watched on photographs since its beginning.

These three photographs cover a period of a year from 9.8.42 (Plate 1), 24.12.42 (Plate 2) to 23.9.43 (Plate 3) and show the early foundations and finally the completed casemates.

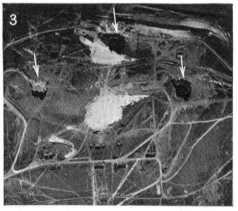

Plate 4 : Elaborate defences in the Boulogne area.
Three-gun light flak (A) : Minefield (B), Anti-tank ditch (C), Six-gun dual purpose A.A./C.D. battery (D), Command Post instruments for battery (E) Wire obstacle (F).

MILITARY INTELLIGENCE
(FROM AIR PHOTOGRAPHS)

As has already been explained, after the fall of France in 1940 all sources of information ceased and air photographs provided the only means of assessing the enemy's intentions. The Army Interpretation Section's primary function at that time was to watch the enemy's military preparations for the invasion of this country. At the same time, however, the enemy was preparing the defences of the Channel coast to which the sobriquet " Festungs Europa " was later applied (*Plates* 1, 2, 3, 4, 7). From the first these defences were carefully plotted on maps, and recorded in dossiers, and gradually a complete picture of them as seen on photographs was built up. (Gradually, of course, as the range of the P.R. aircraft increased German territory was dealt with in the same way (*Plates* 5, 6). So that at any time a report could be given immediately on the state of the defences in any given area. This proved its value, particularly during the first half of 1942, when the Army Section provided a large proportion of the intelligence for the Commando raids at Bruneval, Le Touquet, Boulogne, St. Nazaire and Dieppe. The work done for Planning Staffs for these operations served to give the section the necessary experience for the major operations which were then envisaged. The landing in North Africa on 8th November, 1942, was the first large-scale landing planned in this country and a vast quantity of intelligence from photographs was supplied for the operation. Only the early planning for the Sicily and Italy landings was done in the U.K. as by that time other A.P.I. Sections had been formed nearer the scene of operations. It was the Normandy landing which provided the culminating point of four years' work, and the basic information for that gigantic operation was obtained from the carefully maintained records. Thus a complete a picture as was possible was provided up to the last minute from the long term study of growing defences to the eleventh hour measures taken by the enemy, such as the beach obstacles which sprang up along the French Coast (*Plate* 9) a few weeks before the invasion of Normandy and also the flooding in coastal regions. Army interpreters now work in the field at Divisional and Corps H.Q. They make a detailed interpretation of the defences opposite the divisional fronts and assist at interrogations and in briefing patrols. The Army photographic centre in the field is invariably situated near the Reconnaissance airfield which also holds the M.F.P.S. (Mobile Field Photographic Section).

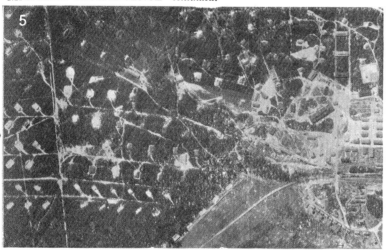

Plate 5: A large ammunition dump in Germany at Lubtheen.

Plate 6: Dragon's Teeth (A) and casemates (B) in the Siegfried Line near Saarbrucken.

Plate 7: Coastal defences at Ostend. Dragon's Teeth (A), road blocks (B). A wall (C) has been built between the Dragon's teeth and the promenade.

Plate 8: A sortie flown 36 hours before the Combined Operations Attack on Dieppe (18.8.42) revealed the tank (lower left corner) in a concrete emplacement and used as a strong point.

Plate 9: Beach obstacles (Element 'C') near Le Treport taken in May, 1944.

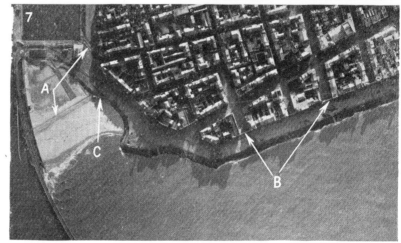

SHIPPING MOVEMENTS

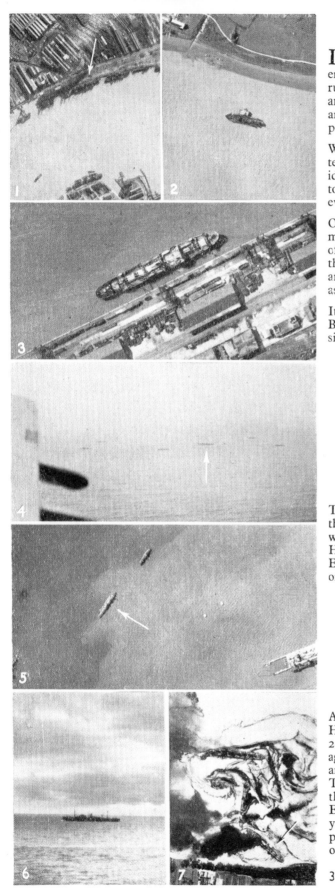

IT was during the winter of 1941/42 that the enemy became boastful about the success of his blockade running to the Far East and, indeed, the number of arrivals and departures of large freighters in Bordeaux and other Biscay ports, as seen on air photographs, gave point to his claims.

With the improvement of cameras and advance in the technique of interpretation, it became possible to identify the great majority of these vessels by name and to determine identification features which were visible even on photographs of small scale or indifferent quality.

Once this was done it became evident that the movements of the ships were largely between the various ports of the French West Coast and from berth to berth within the same port and that the number of departures and arrivals to and from the Far East was not so impressive as had been feared.

It was soon obvious that these vessels, whilst in the Biscay ports, were undergoing a fixed routine which can simply be summarised as:

Stage 1. Dockyard for overhaul.
   ,,   2. Dry dock for bottom cleaning.
   ,,   3. Dockyard for adjustments.
   ,,   4. Bassens North (Bordeaux) for loading.
   ,,   5. Customs House Quay (Bordeaux) where they could lie in deep water and presumably be under guard.
   ,,   6. Departure — a stage sometimes recorded on photographs taken by patrolling aircraft of Coastal Command.

Thus it was a simple matter for the Interpreter to report the stage of readiness of each vessel. Such a routine was watched during the preparation of the Italian HIMALAYA, a modern motor ship of 6,250 g.r.t. Examples of some stages in her preparation are shown on the left.

Plate 1. In dockyard hands at Bordeaux 15.11.42.
   ,,   2. Docked at Pauillac 23.11.42.
   ,,   3. Lying off, presumably laden at Bassens North, Bordeaux, 18.3.43.
   ,,   4. Photographed in the Bay on 29.3.43 by a Coastal Command aircraft from Mount Batten. She is escorted by a considerable force of destroyers and torpedo boats.

After this sighting the convoy returned and the HIMALAYA was seen lying off La Pallice on 2.4.43. (Plate 5). She set out again later, when she was again sighted by Coastal Command on 10.4.43 (Plate 6) and she again put back to the safety of the Gironde. This second unsuccessful attempt was the last effort on the part of the enemy to send a blockade runner to the East. The HIMALAYA eventually joined the graveyard of scuttled vessels below Bordeaux where she was photographed on 26.8.44 surrounded by smoke, oil and other sinking ships (Plate 7).

30

The German MUNSTERLAND, a vessel of 6,400 g.r.t. achieved some success on the route to the Far East. *Plate* 1 shows her inward bound to Bordeaux during May, 1942. She is seen under attack by an anti U-boat aircraft of the R.A.A.F. operating with Coastal Command. Probably damaged, but able to continue, she reached Bordeaux and berthed at the Customs House Quays where she unloaded (*Plate* 2) and then moved up to the dockyard at Nantes where she underwent extensive refit — and no doubt repair (*Plate* 3). Later she duly moved to dock, using the large floating dock at Pauillac (*Plate* 4, 14.3.43) but she did not go back to the dockyard nor move to the customary loading berth. Instead she remained at Bordeaux for 5 months and then was once more docked. Meanwhile the losses amongst blockade runners on the high seas had, no doubt, led to a revision of the enemy's plans and in October, 1943, the MUNSTERLAND moved up the coast, destined for German waters. She was attacked in Cherbourg by aircraft of Fighter Command (*Plate* 5) and this necessitated a visit to dock in that port for repairs (*Plate* 6); repairs completed she moved to Dieppe and thence to Boulogne where she stayed from Jan. 1st to Jan. 20th, 1944— a hesitation no doubt dictated by the advantages of a moonless night for the passage through the Straits. On 20th January she continued eastward but was immediately sunk by our Coastal artillery and the wreck was found by an American recce. plane the next morning (*Plate* 7) and by Typhoons of Fighter Command who gave her a last beating-up and recorded their target on cine camera guns (*Plate* 8).

The ALSTERUFER, a modern German fruiter of only 2,729 g.r.t., was not regarded as a potential Blockade Runner when she lay inactive at Nantes until early in 1943 (*Plate* 1). When she moved to a dockyard berth in February (*Plate* 2), it was thought that she might be going to be commissioned as a Sperrbrecher, like others of her type and size. Almost immediately, however, she moved to the loading quay at BORDEAUX (*Plate* 3, 14.3.43) and suspicions were confirmed when she left the area, during a spell of cloudy weather at the end of March, in company with the OSORNO and the PORTLAND. The outward journey was successful for ALSTERUFER and OSORNO but the return to Europe of ALSTER-UFER, OSORNO, WESSERLAND, RIO GRANDE and BURGENLAND at the end of 1943 was the last disastrous phase of the Far East — France service. Only OSORNO made port and she was mined at the entrance to the Gironde. ALSTERUFER outlived three of her companions but on 27.12.43 she was spotted and attacked by aircraft of Coastal Command operating five or six hundred miles out in the Atlantic. Her end came when aircraft H of 311 Squadron hit her with a bomb (*Plate* 4) and caused a fire which became out of control (*Plate* 5). It is probable that the crew found scuttling the only solution to their unenviable position and fired the bridge before taking to the boats.

RESEARCH ON ENEMY WARSHIPS
(FROM AIR PHOTOGRAPHS)

Although many hundreds of air photographs of enemy warships have been taken, the information sought has normally related to their whereabouts rather than to features of their design; such detail usually was known already. Very occasionally, however, photographs have revealed something quite new, such as a new type or class, or a novel arrangement or rearrangement of armament. When such information as this turns up, air photography becomes a very valuable medium of Naval intelligence.

In previous wars, such information was sometimes obtained from agents and was frequently unreliable or was never obtained at all. Now, air photography supplies the data for the preparation of recognition material on enemy navies for the benefit of photographic interpreters, intelligence officers and aircrews, as well as for the use of the Royal Navy. Photographs taken from the air enable ship recognition material to be kept up-to-date as new types of ships or modifications to existing types appear, in addition to revealing new construction and armament policies on the part of the enemy.

Among the more important of the earlier discoveries in German ports was the fact that the 'Tirpitz' was on the point of completion early in 1941. At a later date, very excellent large-scale photographs of the 'Tirpitz' were obtained (Plate 1) from which the armament layout could be studied. Accurate measurements could also be made which showed that her tonnage exceeded 40,000, although she was officially built under international convention, to 35,000 tons.

Another discovery was that the only German aircraft carrier, the 'Graf Zeppelin,' though well-advanced, was evidently not being completed. Reconnaissance also

PLATE 1

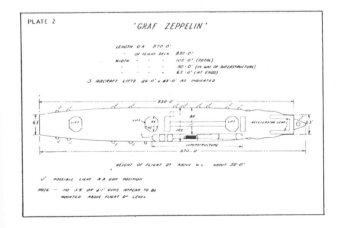

PLATE 2   'GRAF ZEPPELIN'

PLATE 2A

showed that the projected sister ships to the 'Tirpitz' and 'Graf Zeppelin' were not being proceeded with.

The Graf Zeppelin was observed to be a larger ship than reported in the naval text books, and sketches and plans were prepared — the first plans of this ship that could be considered authentic, since the photographs were carefully measured (*Plates* 2 & 2A). Apart from this very large unit, it was among the smaller vessels that anything novel was likely to occur, and it was in this category that most of the discoveries were made. The different sub-classes of the " Narvik " type destroyers and the variant later known as the " Seetier " class were duly revealed. The first sortie flown over the port of Elbing in the Baltic in August, 1942, revealed for the first time an entirely new class of smaller German destroyer, which took their class name from the port of construction. (*Plates* 3 & 3A).

When photographs of the Italian ports began to come in, many interesting ships were revealed, from battle-ships down to torpedo boats and small auxiliaries. Apart from certain details in the battleships which differed in actual fact from published data, the most important new ships from the point of design and armament revealed by air photographs were the light cruisers of the Regolo class (*Plates* 4 & 4A).

It is of interest to note that information was obtained about some Italian naval units that were hitherto un-known and plans of them were drawn entirely from air photographs (e.g., the escort vessel Diana — see *Plate* 4A) and that only when all the Italian ports were covered, was it possible for us to know what was the full active strength of the Italian Navy.

As to the Japanese Navy, a considerable amount of instructional and recognition material has been prepared with the aid of air photographs from American sources. Even though such information is ' second-hand,' some research has been made on Japanese naval construction.

In conclusion, it may be said that, without the aid of air photography, our knowledge of new enemy develop-ments in warship design and armament would have been most limited.

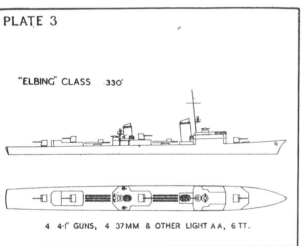

PLATE 3

"ELBING" CLASS .330'

4 4·1" GUNS, 4 37MM & OTHER LIGHT AA, 6 TT.

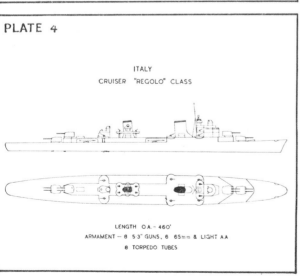

PLATE 4

ITALY
CRUISER "REGOLO" CLASS

LENGTH O.A. - 460'
ARMAMENT — 8 5.3" GUNS, 6 65mm & LIGHT AA
8 TORPEDO TUBES

PLATE 3A

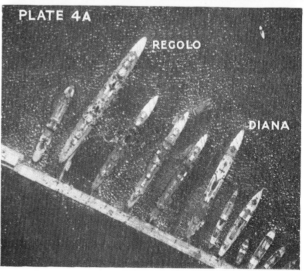

PLATE 4A

REGOLO

DIANA

AIRCRAFT AND THE AIRCRAFT INDUSTRY

By means of photographic reconnaissance a constant watch has been maintained on the enemy's air power. Use of stereo cover and shadows to reveal the third dimension has enabled interpreters to report accurately wing-span, length, dihedral and other characteristics of enemy aircraft. Additional data about known types and their development has been recorded, while new types have been detected and closely followed to operational status. The aircraft industry has come under a similar close scrutiny, factories and production centres being successfully located so that blows could be struck at the source. An example is the following story of the discovery of the Me 262 :

"A medium twin engined aircraft of unusual design has been photographed twice at LECHFELD airfield and an aircraft of the same type was also seen recently near the Messerschmitt experimental hangars at AUGSBURG. There are indications that this aircraft which will be known as the 'LECHFELD 42' may possibly be jet propelled . . . . ."

(Extract from P.I. report FEB. 1944)

This new aircraft was later established as the twin jet propelled Me 262, and its development to operational status closely watched.

(*Plate* 1) Increasing numbers reported at LECHFELD A/F. (*Plate* 2) The Me 262 is seen eventually at the RECHLIN/LARZ experimental airfield in N.W. Germany. (*Plate* 3) The constant look-out for the tell-tale jet marks reveals a front line base at HOPSTEN A/F. (*Plate* 4) Intensified Me 262 activity reported at SCHWABISCH/HALL airfield.

Factory dispersal following ceaseless attacks on the production centres led to the discovery of an improvised Me 262 assembly factory at LEIPHEIM A/F (*Plate* 5), and a former shoe factory at WASSERBERG (*Plate* 6) nearby was found to have converted to Me 262 production. Photographic evidence also went towards confirming that the agricultural implement factory at BAUMENHEIM (*Plate* 7) had been similarly commandeered. Finally close scrutiny of activity reported in and around the road tunnels at ESCHENLOHE (*Plate* 8) in the Bavarian Alps revealed that Me 262 production had been eventually driven underground.

LECHFELD

RECHLIN/LARZ

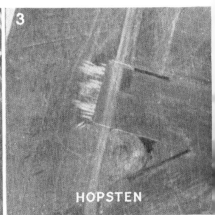

HOPSTEN

SCHWABISCH-HALL

LEIPHEIM

6

Factory

WASSERBURG

7

Factory

BAUMENHEIM

8

Tunnel Entrances

ESCHENLOHE

MESSERSCHMITT UNDERGROUND FACTORY

WATCHING THE AIRFIELDS

In this war a detailed knowledge of the state and disposition of the enemy's airfields has been indispensable in the planning and carrying out of operations. That this information has been and is being obtained is due almost solely to the work of P.R.U. and of its allied interpretation units. Regular flying reconnaissance programmes ensure that full and accurate information is kept up to date on all airfields, landing grounds and seaplane bases in enemy and enemy-occupied countries.

Throughout the whole progress of this struggle factual and photographic material has instantly been available when required on any of the Luftwaffe bases. Expansion of existing airfields and the construction of new ones were closely watched, battle order constantly checked and details of serviceability and capacity carefully tabulated. Indications of future enemy plans were often revealed by modifications to or expansion of his existing airfield situation. A good example of the growth of an airfield is afforded by photographs taken over a period of approximately 3 years (*Plates* 1, 2 and 3). On August 1st, 1940, cover revealed a certain amount of hedge clearance near the village of KERLIN/BASTARD near Lorient (*Plate* 1). Subsequent covers revealed that an airfield was projected, and by June, 1941 (*Plate* 2) it was evident that when finished it would rank high in importance in the scale of Luftwaffe bases. Ground intelligence and types of aircraft that appeared as soon as runways and installations were serviceable identified it as a shipping reconnaissance base and a powerful aid to Bordeaux/Merignac that hitherto had been the chief German counterpart to our Coastal Command in the Biscay area. *Plate* 3 shows the airfield in advanced stage of construction in April, 1943.

Enemy camouflage has often been exceedingly good and airfields invisible to the naked eye of the high flying pilot have often been picked up by photographs. *Plates* 4 and 5 illustrate this: clever simulation by spraying and painting of the pattern of the surrounding countryside on the landing ground at Laval makes it very unobtrusive.

The increasingly heavy bomber raids by day and night into Germany in 1943 necessitated the regrouping of the Luftwaffe interception units in France and even bomber airfields were utilised, as at Nantes/Chateau Bougon where fighter squadrons were formed along the edge of the airfield complete with dispersal shelters in readiness for the take-off (*Plate* 6).

Sure sign that the saturation bombing of airfields was destroying far too many aircraft on the ground was vividly illustrated in 1943 by the photographic cover of numerous new dispersal areas covering extensive stretches of the surrounding countryside. Such photographic evidence is obviously, invaluable for briefing low flying 'strikes'. *Plate* 7 shows the elaborate and extensive spread of taxi tracks (*arrows*) for aircraft dispersal away from the airfield (A) at Montelimar.

Plate 4 : The landing ground at Laval with a painted pattern of fields, hedges and bushes to merge in with the surrounding features. Compare this with a photograph taken a year later (Plate 5), the camouflage has worn off and the landing ground is clearly visible.

Plate 6 : Fighters and fighter aircraft shelters on the edge of the bomber airfield at Nantes/Chateau Bougon during 1943 when allied bombing was developing in strength.

Plate 7 : Widespread dispersal (arrows) at Montelimar airfield (A), also a result of the ever increasing Allied bombing offensive and destruction of aircraft on airfields.

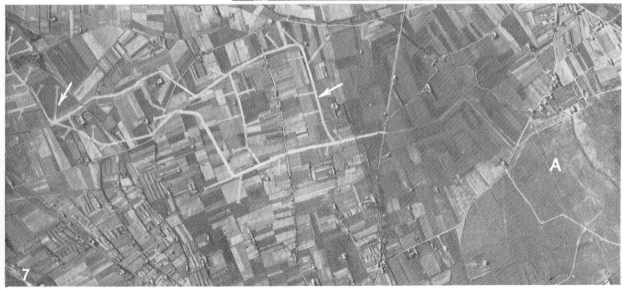

INDUSTRY

Air photographs have proved a major source of information regarding German industry. The example given below is of the largest synthetic oil plant known to be in existence, at BRUX in SUDETENLAND.

Up to May, 1942, Intelligence sources had indicated the presence of a new synthetic oil plant near BRUX in SUDETENLAND, but there was no information as to its exact position, size and state. Its output was guessed at 240,000 tons per annum, and it was presumed to be producing oil. The first photographic cover of the plant, obtained in May, 1942, showed the truth to be very different. The plant was not, in fact completed and its size was far greater than had been previously indicated, occupying a site about 1½ miles square. Careful analysis of the photographs showed that the plant was designed for an initial production of 750,000 tons per annum, which made it equal to the largest plants in existence elsewhere. It was further observed that production of oil was likely to start in about six months, while some tar was already being processed. The second cover, eleven months later revealed that operations had begun and that production was at the rate of 20% of the total. It showed a feature which had not been expected, that the equipment installed up to 1942 was only the first stage of construction and that extensions were already beginning to increase the potential output to the enormous total of 1,250,000 tons per annum, much greater than any other synthetic oil plant in existence. From that time onwards P.R. sorties made it possible to trace the increase in output as successive items of the plant were brought into operation, until

early in 1944 the output was estimated at 700,000 tons per annum.

Interpretation of the photographs had revealed one highly vulnerable section of the works. The whole of the gas generating was concentrated in a single area about 200 feet square and there was no possible alternative supply available. This then was the pinpoint objective when the plant was first attacked in May, 1944, and the result was highly satisfactory. Although the raid was light in proportion to the area of the works, the gas generators were seriously damaged and the whole plant was put out of action for more than two months, when it was again attacked successfully. Since then there have been repeated attempts to repair the plant, but photographic reconnaissance maintained a close watch on such efforts so that production has never been achieved for more than a few days or weeks before fresh damage has been inflicted to put the works out of action once more. The latest attacks were much heavier than the earlier ones and have inflicted major damage to high pressure equipment which is difficult to replace. Detailed knowledge of the function of each part of the works has made possible continuous forecasts of the length of the shut-down period after each raid and make it possible to say now with reasonable accuracy that the plant has been put out of action for at least three months.

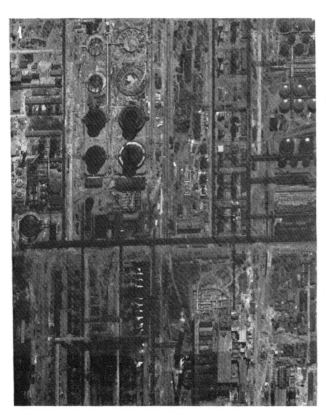
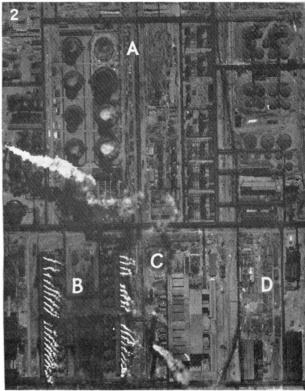

3

Hydrogenation Stalls

Refinery

Cooling Towers

Power Plant

Tar Plant

Gas Plant

ILLUSTRATIONS

Plate 1 : Part of the BRUX plant taken from the first photographic cover to be obtained, in May, 1942.
Plate 2 : The second cover of the plant showed completion of many structures (examples lettered) with additional work still in progress.
Plate 3 : (above) The enormous plant in operation a few weeks before the first attack was made. The continuous building of new hydrogenation stalls gave a clue to the tremendous output the Germans had in view but which was never attained.

ENEMY COMMUNICATIONS

Aerial photography has been extensively used to obtain information regarding railways and waterways in Germany and enemy occupied territories and was almost the sole source of such information prior to the invasion of Western Europe by Allied Forces in 1944. From frequent reconnaissance of railway centres it was possible to prepare and issue interpretation reports giving detailed information of traffic concentrations and movements. Comparison of the information for successive covers enabled valuable data, as to the extent to which the various centres were being used by the enemy, to be obtained. Aerial photographs also furnished detailed information of the layout and exact location of Marshalling Yards, Locomotive Depots, Sidings, Bridges and other facilities along the enemy lines of communication, which were still being used for the planning of bombing attack, to disrupt the flow of enemy traffic. From aerial photographs taken after the attacks it has been possible to assess the extent of the interruption to traffic and the speed at which facilities were restored to use.

Plate 1 : An oblique shot by a reconnaissance aircraft of the destruction of the rail and road bridge of Rouen/Oissel.

Plate 2 : Amiens/Longueau marshalling yard following two concentrated attacks by aircraft of Bomber Command at a time when the yard was heavily loaded with a variety of rolling stock.

Plate 3 : A close-up of part of a military train showing flats loaded with tanks and assault guns.

COMMUNICATIONS—*continued.*

Both before and after the Allied invasion of France, systematic reconnaissance of railway lines used by the enemy has supplied valuable information regarding military movements. Other military information obtained includes the location and nature of railway guns used as defences against Allied air attacks.

New construction along certain lines revealed by aerial photographs has been an indication of the importance of such lines to the enemy, while the removal of track from other lines has indicated their relative importance and also the enemy's shortage of rails.

Inland waterways in Germany, the Low Countries, France, etc., have also been under constant observation for the movement and nature of traffic. In addition particular studies have been made to discover such vulnerable points as aqueducts, locks, embanked stretches, etc., which could be destroyed by bombing attacks and so interrupt movement along the waterways. Similarly bridges have been located as targets for the interruption, by bombing attacks, of rail or road traffic over waterways.

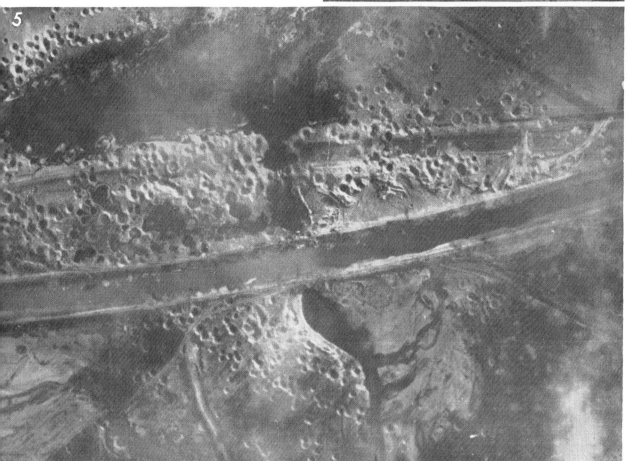

Plate 4 : *The embanked stretch of the Mittelland canal near Gravenhorst was chosen as a vulnerable point and has been successfully attacked. Reconstruction work is shown in progress following the last raid.*

Plate 5 : *The closing of the Dortmund-Ems Canal near Ladbergen by bombing the embankment and the aqueduct disrupted traffic all over N.W. Germany. Repair work after each raid had been closely watched, and is shown here in an advanced stage a month after the last attack.*

THE BATTLE AGAINST THE FLYING BOMB

In most operations which have taken place during this war photographic reconnaissance has played a greater or lesser part, but in no other major operation has that part been so complete or all embracing as in the battle against the flying bomb. To P.R. and P.I. fell the task, first of identifying the weapons with which we had to contend and then of directing the necessary counter measures. At all stages of this battle — experimental, manufacture, storage and operational — a ceaseless vigil was kept, no matter how remote the area. P.I. findings and subsequent targetting enabled the Allied Bomber Commands to harass such activity incessantly, to cause the abandonment of many installations and to retard the German operational programme for many months. Ground intelligence, very early in 1943 had indicated that secret experimental work was in hand at PEENEMUNDE, work connected with the manufacture and perfection of a secret weapon on which high hopes were placed, though no details as to its form or performance were available. Immediate attention was paid to this part of the world, and regular cover was flown to watch developments. Certain installations became suspect though their use was unexplained (*Plate* 1) and interest in this area was intensified. In November, 1943, cover was obtained of ZINNOWITZ, another Baltic experimental station and 'ramps' similar to those at Peenemunde were also observed (*Plate* 2).

For some months certain "constructional works" of unidentified purpose had been under construction in the PAS DE CALAIS and elsewhere in N.W. France. Parallels were drawn between these and the installations at Peenemunde. The appearance of the first flying bomb on one of the ramps at Peenemunde immediately solved the puzzle (*Plate* 3). All those "unidentified military constructions" in N.W. France were explained and their dangerous character revealed as launching sites for the flying bomb. Between October, 1943 and January, 1944, all 96 of these firing sites — the BOIS CARRE type — were detected, photographed and targetted, as the result of a colossal reconnaissance programme. All were continually bombed and not one was allowed to fire in its original form (*Plates* 4, 5 *and* 6).

This type of firing site was obviously too difficult to conceal owing to its layout and the multiplicity of standard buildings. The Germans accordingly adopted a modified pattern — the BELHAMELIN. All non-essential buildings were cut out and in an effort at greater concealment the greatest possible use was made of woods and orchards (*Plate* 7). Ramps often followed the lines of roads and large farm buildings were frequently used to house a complete unit of the firing site (*Plate* 9). Between May and September, 1944, a total of 133 Belhamelin type firing sites were discovered from photographs, pin pointed and targetted. The whole of the so-called 'Rocket Coast' was flown incessantly so that the state of serviceability of any one site was alway known. Bombing to the best advantage in the months that followed, bombing that ensured that only about one third of the sites were usually able to fire at any one time.

An essential part of the battle was the location of manufacture, supply and storage depots for the flying bombs. As all dumps were situated underground in an effort to escape bombing, ground information generally led to the discovery of such storage sites. Photographic cover was ceaselessly being searched to prove or disprove such reports. A typical storage site was that at ST. LEU D'ESSERENT (*Plate* 10) where old mushroom caves were taken over, enlarged and entrances fortified by steel and concrete doors. Invaluable information was gathered by low flying pilots who took remarkable obliques showing amount of overhang over tunnels and other technical data necessary for the best bombing results (*Plates* 11 *and* 12).

Heavy bombing followed targetting (*Plate* 13) and it is significant that following the bombing of ST. LEU D'ESSERENT the number of flying bomb incidents in Britain fell considerably. When the battle against the ground-launched flying bomb was finally over following the liberation of the PAS DE CALAIS, a total of well over 3,000 sorties had been flown and over 1,200,000 prints interpreted.

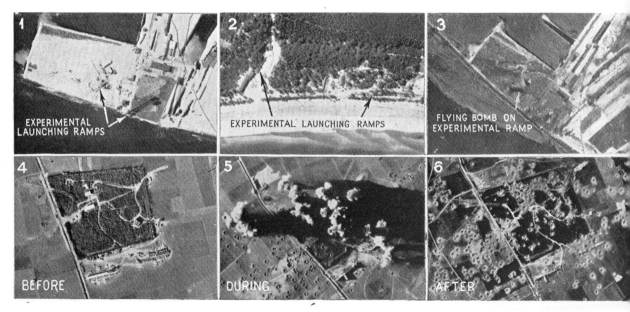

1 EXPERIMENTAL LAUNCHING RAMPS

2 EXPERIMENTAL LAUNCHING RAMPS

3 FLYING BOMB ON EXPERIMENTAL RAMP

4 BEFORE

5 DURING

6 AFTER

7

FLYING BOMB ON RAMP

8

LAUNCHING RAMP

SERVICING BUILDING
UNDER EXISTING BARN

9

(8) AFTER BOMBING

10

ENTRANCES

11

ENTRANCE

SLIDING REINFORCED
CONCRETE DOOR

12

ENTRANCE

PILL BOX

13

SUBSIDENCE

SUBSIDENCE

ENTRANCES

(10) AFTER BOMBING

EARLY DISCOVERY OF GERMAN RADAR

THE first evidence of the use of Radar by the enemy was gained from these photographs covering the Cap de la Hague peninsula. It is interesting to note the scale of the photographs from which this first information was obtained. *Plate* 1 is a photograph reproduced at the same scale as that at which interpretation was done; it is from a sortie flown on 22.11.40 and revealed two circular objects which raised suspicions (See inset 1A an enlargement from the same negative showing detail). it was also noticed that in the nine seconds interval between two exposures of the objects that the shadow thrown by some form of superstructure had slightly changed in shape, indicating movement, most probably around a vertical axis. It was thought at that time that the site was not unlike a flak position, though the nearness to each other of the objects and the lack of the usual track activity on a flak site ruled out this possibility. Previous cover was inspected and a photograph of the same area (*Plate* 2) taken a few weeks earlier on 5.10.40 showed no trace of the objects. The unusual appearance of the site together with the fact that this was considered an area to be concerned with radio research caused a secret report to be sent to the radio experts at the Air Ministry. They at once considered it to be of sufficient importance to request, though with diffidence in view of the obvious hazards involved, special low altitude obliques to be taken. This was done a few days later on 16.2.41, when, in spite of a gallant effort on the part of the pilot, chance robbed it of the success it deserved. The aircraft was, in fact, travelling too fast for the camera so that no overlap of exposures was possible and the objective only appeared partially on the extreme edge of the print. The pilot reported that flak, from the position, seen to the right in *Plate* 3, was in action against him without success. Six days later on 22.2.41 a magnificent low oblique was obtained (*Plate* 4) giving adequate proof that the enemy was using radio detection of our aircraft.

Besides data on probable frequencies used, etc., obtainable by measurements of the aerial arrays on the oblique photograph, vertical photographs were used to produce a contour map of the area so that study of the land formation made it possible for experts to deduct the characteristics of the wave forms transmitted.

(The spectacular oblique photographs (*Plates* 3 *and* 4) were taken from a Spitfire with a side facing oblique F.24 Camera.).

AIR PHOTOGRAPHY AND "D"-DAY

The first two requirements from air photographs for the planning of the invasion of Europe in 1944 related to beaches and defences. Photographs of all beaches in the proposed areas were closely studied and those suitable for landing purposes finally selected. This was followed by detailed interpretation of the complex defence systems which formed the so-called "Atlantic Wall." Later even more detailed interpretation was needed on exits, routes, dispersal areas, bridging requirements, etc. Sites of the landing strips for aircraft were also chosen from air photographs and in the same way were selected the dropping and landing zones for the paratroops and airborne forces. From July, 1942 onwards models were produced, at first of general areas at small scale but later of all the landing beaches and dropping zones to a larger scale. These models were constructed from maps and aerial photographs, at scales adequate to show in three dimensions all land form, surface workings, trees, buildings, fields, beaches and defences, etc. The models were reproduced in quantity and eventually used, along with thousands of copies of the actual photographs, for the briefing of all forces during the week that preceded " D "-Day.

(Plate 1.) An oblique view looking east of the model of a heavy gun battery on the Normandy coast east of the Caen Canal.

(Plate 2.) A vertical view of the model of a strip of the Normandy coast at Ouistreham (A) at the mouth of the Caen Canal. The heavy gun battery is seen at (B).

(Plate 3.) A vertical photograph of the gun battery taken in May 1944 showing the effects of Allied air bombardment.

Continued on the following two pages.

(Plate 4.) *The dropping zones—parachutes scattered over the ground near Ranville on the 6th June, 1944. Gliders were also landed on this area.*

(Plate 5.) *The landing zones—part of a concentration of gliders which landed east of the Caen Canal south of Ouistreham photographed on "D"-Day.*

(Plate 6.) *The landing strips—a completed landing strip for aircraft built on the cliff top west of Port en Bassin, photographed in September. All the research and survey for these dropping zones, landing zones and landing strips were prepared from reconnaissance photographs flown over the Normandy area prior to " D "-Day.*

(Plate 7.) The landing beaches—a vertical photograph taken on the 6th June, 1944, of the landing beach at Graye sur Mer west of Ouistreham showing empty landing craft and a concentration of vehicles and equipment on the shore. This was one of the many landing beaches selected and planned from aerial photographs long before " D "-Day.

TOWN PLANNING

Aerial photography and interpretation, which have both developed powerfully as weapons of war, have also manifold applications in planning for peace.

Town planning is one field in which their value is already recognised. The legacies of the historic past and the evidences of present use are brought equally vividly into the planner's vision.

Here we may note how LA ROCHE SUR YON (population 13,600) laid out by Napoleon I in 1804 as a new departmental capital, still has much garden space within its tree-lined pentagonal boulevard while its modern additions straggle untidily into the surrounding landscape.

In contrast, AVOLA in Sicily (population 19,000), rebuilt after the great earthquake of 1693 on a most original plan with a hexagonal core, enclosing 5 piazzas, has a densely-built surrounding zone of gardenless dwellings in monotonous rows, which gives way abruptly to the almond orchards beyond.

48